Learn about

NUMBERS

"Poldy" is a trademark
of World Book, Inc.

World Book, Inc.
525 W. Monroe
Chicago, IL 60661

For information on other
World Book products,
call 1-800-255-1750.

ISBN: 0-7166-6104-7
LC: 95-61311

Printed in Mexico

1 2 3 4 5 6 7 8 9 10 99 98 97 96 95

Learn about

NUMBERS

World Book, Inc.
a Scott Fetzer company
Chicago London Sydney Toronto

Meet Poldy
and his friends

Poldy the scarecrow was made to scare birds away from a farmer's field. But the birds were not frightened by Poldy. In fact, three birds named Wagtail, Crow, and Seagull became his friends.

When the weather grew cold, Poldy's friends prepared to fly away to wonderful, warm places all over the world. The three birds wanted Poldy to go with them, so they worked together to teach him how to fly. Then Poldy and his friends flew away to see and learn about the world.

In **Learn about Numbers**, Poldy and his friends explore India.

"You're just in time," said a peacock. "Just in time for the big parade. It will start from here in one minute."

Poldy and the birds looked
around. "A parade?" asked
Crow. "Where is everyone?"

"**I'm** the parade," said the peacock proudly, spreading his feathers into a colorful fan. "You may join my parade if you wish, but please stay well behind me."

The peacock set off,
strutting down the middle
of the road.

"That's a silly parade," jeered
Seagull. "And **I'm** certainly not
joining in."

"I must agree," said Crow,
"that a parade of one is a very
strange sight."

"Is this a parade?" asked
a deep voice behind them.
"May we join in?" asked
another.
Poldy and the birds turned
to see two huge elephants.

"Of course you may," said Wagtail. "Two elephants are just what we need."

"Then climb up," said the
elephants, "and we'll be off."

"Oh, look at that parade!" cried three women, as they filled their water pots at the well. "May we come along?"

"Of course!" boomed the elephants. "But stay well behind. We don't want to step on your saris."

"Oh, look!" cried four water buffaloes in a nearby field. "It's a parade. May we join in?"

"Of course you may," said the women in their saris. "But please stay well behind with those muddy feet."

Five monkeys looked down from the roof of a temple. They pointed their fingers and laughed. "One, two, three, four. What you need are five more," they called.

"Very well," snorted the buffaloes, "but stay well behind and don't try any monkey business."

It really was a very good parade, and everything was going well until . . .

"**Stop!**" roared a tiger, rolling his eyes. "No one comes past here until I've had my supper."

"Help!" squeaked the peacock, backing onto the elephants' trunks.

"Stop!" trumpeted the elephants, sitting on the women's saris.

"Oops!" cried the women, slipping in the buffaloes' mud.

"Whoa!" warned the buffaloes, treading on the monkeys' tails.

"Eek!" squealed the monkeys, leaping up a nearby fruit tree.

Some pieces of fruit crashed
to the ground, bounced several
times, and rolled toward the
tiger.
   The tiger didn't wait. He was
off in a flash!

"All right!" said the peacock, as he dusted himself off and straightened his feathers. "If you're all quite ready, we will continue our parade. Everyone join in—but please stay well behind!"

The photo

"Where is everyone?" asked Poldy. "Please take your seats for the photo!"

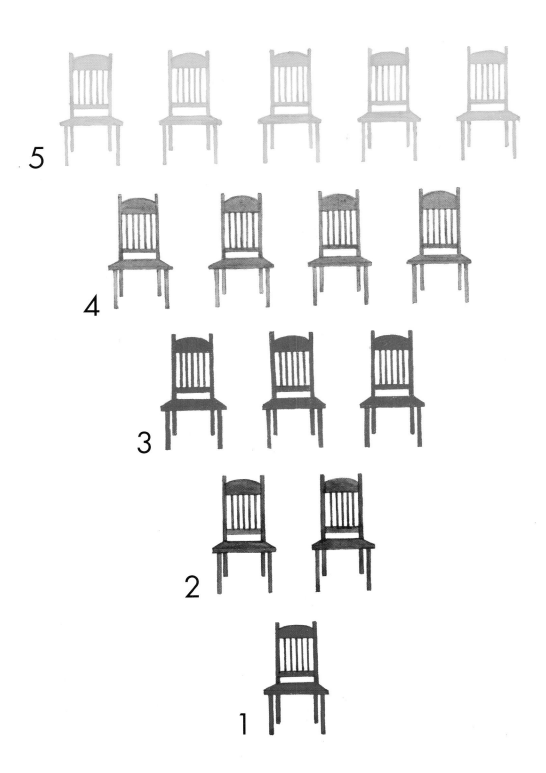

5

4

3

2

1

"I will sit here," said the peacock, "because I am the star of the show."

There are two chairs for two elephants.

There are three chairs
for three women.

"Please ask the water
buffaloes to take their
seats," said Poldy.

There is one chair for each
of the monkeys.

"Smile, please," said Poldy.
CLICK!

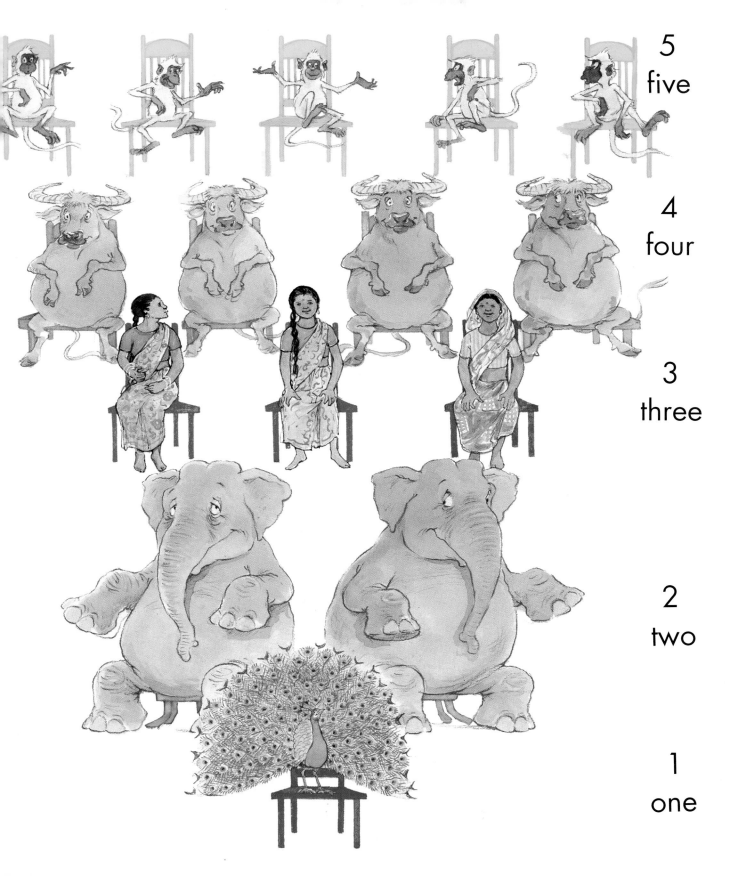

5
five

4
four

3
three

2
two

1
one

Parent notes

Numbers are a part of our everyday lives. Counting, matching, and sorting are among the most important skills children can learn during their preschool years. **Learn about Numbers** introduces your child to the numbers one through five as Poldy and his friends join in a parade. On every page, there are things to look at and count.

Your child will enjoy the story and pictures for their own sake, but with your encouragement, this book will be a valuable learning aid. Take every opportunity to count the animals or people on a page. Look for other objects in the pictures. Count each set of objects as it is introduced. Try to repeat the sequence of numbers from one to five each time, to reinforce the counting activity.

At the end of the book, there is a photograph page. There the words *one* through *five* are brought together with the figures 1 through 5. This provides an opportunity for you and your child to count, match, and sort. Here are some questions you might like to consider:

All about the chairs

How many chairs have elephants on them?
How many green chairs are there?
Which row has the most chairs?
How many chairs have animals on them?

All about the animals

How many animals are there with two legs?
How many animals are there with four legs?
How many animals can you see with tails?
How many animals have trunks?

Learning together

You can use the story as a starting point for other counting, matching, and sorting activities.

Cut up old magazines and sort the pictures into sets of different objects. Use these pictures to make a picture collage of a parade.

When you are out walking, look for numbers on clocks, road signs, car license plates, telephones, price tags, and calendars.

Encourage your child to help you set the table for a meal. How many people will there be? Is there a plate for each person?